FO

Hello!
Thanks for reading
"Trev and Simon's Stupid Book!"
Well, we hope you've read it! You may have
just found it lying around in a friend's
bathroom, or in an old dustbin!
Whatever, we hope you enjoy it!
We hope you enjoy it so much that you will
want to read it again and again.
We hope you read it until it falls to bits
and you have to go out and buy another copy,
or until your bottom bursts!

HAVE FUN!!!

Trev and Simon's
STUPID BOOK

Trevor Neal and Simon Hickson

Designed by the authors

Illustrated by the authors,
Jane Laycock and John C. Kerr

RED FOX

A Red Fox Book
Published by Arrow Books Limited
20 Vauxhall Bridge Road, London SW1V 2SA

An imprint of the Random Century Group

London Melbourne Sydney Auckland
Johannesburg and agencies throughout the world

Red Fox edition 1990

No copies of this book will be sold in South Africa

Set in Century Schoolbook
by JH Graphics Ltd, Reading

Made and printed in Great Britain by
The Guernsey Press Co Ltd
Guernsey C.I.

ISBN 0 09 975090 2

ACKNOWLEDGEMENTS

Trev and Simon
would like to acknowledge
the fact
that this book
is
stupid!

The authors' and publisher's thanks to the following for the supply of clothes and props for the cover photographs:

FRONT COVER

CLOTHES
Gold and silver leather tasselled jackets from Johnsons
Black and white squiggly shirts from Johnsons
PROPS
'Big Head' comb and 'Big Mouth' toothbrush from Cascade

BACK COVER (top right to bottom)

CLOTHES
Silver hat from Hyper Hyper by Yvonne Rohe
Squiggly black and white shirts from Johnsons
Red and purple bomber jackets from Boy
Green and red silk T-shirts from Browns by Go Silk
Flowery shirt from Top Man
'Games' shirts from Liberty's by Muschino
Gold and silver tasselled jackets from Johnsons
PROPS
Duck / crocodile glove puppets / large, yellow glasses from Covent Garden General Store
'Big Head' comb and 'Big Mouth' toothbrush from Cascade

CONTENTS

HAVE FUN!!!

Which is little Jimmy's balloon?

←Eiffel Tower

CAN YOU SPEAK FRENCH?

TRY OUR SIMPLE QUIZ TO FIND OUT
IF YOU CAN SPEAK FRENCH!!!

Question one

Can you speak French?

A) Oui

B) No

How well did you do?

If you scored mostly 'A' – Well done! your French is so good, people must often come up to you and ask 'Excuse me, but are you French?'

If you scored mostly 'B' – Hard luck! You can't speak French at all. In fact, you're rubbish at it. But keep on trying!!!

Now try the quiz out on your friends!

PERSONALISE YOUR OWN THINGS

Imagine your favourite book!

Imagine your favourite jumper!!

Imagine your favourite pair of pants!!!

Now imagine all these favourite things of yours with your own name across the front!

Here also!!!

Your name here!

Your name here!

And here!

Yes! Now you can give all of your belongings your own personal stamp of identity with this unique PEN!!!

Buy two and write your name here as well!!!

How does it work??? It's simple!!!

All you have to do is simply take the unique PEN and write YOUR NAME on everything you own! It's as easy as ABC!

To obtain this unique self-personalising PEN, just send lots and lots of money to:

STUPID RIP-OFF PEN OFFER, PO BOX BIG-CON, GET-RICH-QUICK, RUN-AWAY-TO-BRAZIL!

Remember – this offer is only available for a limited period and only through this book! Send your money off now!!!

WAITER·WAITER FUN

Waiter, waiter,
Do you have frog's legs?
Yes sir, I'm afraid I was the victim
of a new genetic engineering
experiment that went
horribly wrong!!!

Waiter, waiter,
There's a fly in my soup!!!
Yes sir, it's fly soup!!!

Waiter, waiter,
There's a fly in my soup!!!
Keep your voice down sir, or
we may be closed down
for failing to meet health
and safety standards!!!

THIS WAY, PLEASE, MADAM!

Waiter, waiter, where's my steak?
I'm sorry sir, but this is a
vegetarian restaurant!

Waiter, waiter, wine for
this table!
I'm sorry sir, but the
licensing laws won't allow
me to serve alcohol at
this late hour!

1962 Supreme Chateau

Waiter, waiter, this soup's cold!!!
No it's not, sir, it's warm ice cream!!!

This page has become too stupid!!!

Waiter, waiter, do you know
Bob Monkhouse?
Indeed I do, sir, I was
a guest on 'Bob Says'

STOP

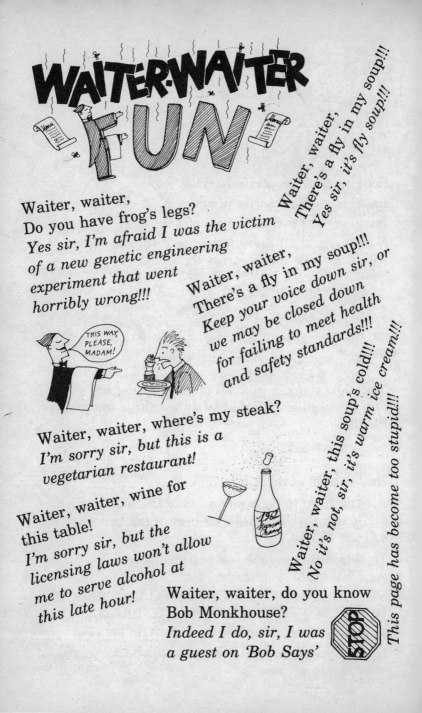

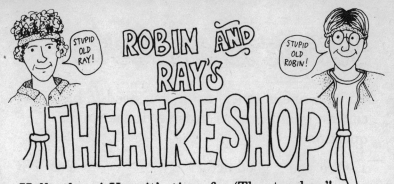

ROBIN AND RAY'S THEATRESHOP

STUPID OLD RAY!

STUPID OLD ROBIN!

Hello there! Yes, it's time for 'Theatreshop'! 'Theatreshop' is all about acting and improvisation, or 'impro' as we call it 'in the business'. 'Impro' means acting and making things up as you go along!

Before any of us do anything vaguely theatrical it's always a good idea to start off with some simple warm-up exercises. Follow the easy routine set out below to get those muscles stretched and supple!

1 Stretch your arms up in the air . . .
2 Stretch up . . .
3 And up . . .
4 And up . . .
5 And hold that position for five seconds . . .
6 And . . . Stretch up . . . And up . . .
7 And collapse in a heap gasping for breath!

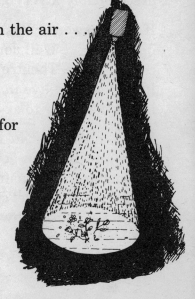

Now we're ready to start acting!

What is an Actor?

To be a fine classical actor you need to have certain qualifications. Answer these simple questions:

1 Are you a good actor?   Yes No

2 Do you have a huge ego?   Yes No

3 Do you have a huge head?   Yes No

4 Do you have a huge collection of
  pastel coloured leisure suits?   Yes No

5 Are you in the Royal Shakespeare
  Company?   Yes No

6 Are you on the dole?   Yes No

If you answered 'Yes' to number six then you are probably a very good actor.

If you answered 'Yes' to any of the other questions . . . Well done! You will enjoy a fine career in the 'Theatre' and will eventually 'get into' films and live in Los Angeles, in a very big house next door to ex-James Bond, Roger Moore!

If you answered 'No' to all the questions, don't worry, anyone can act! Yes, even you! So go and get changed into your turquoise velveteen leisure suits and let's begin the 'Theatreshop' Crash Course— **'How to be a Good Actor, the Quick Way!**

HOW TO BE A GOOD ACTOR – THE QUICK WAY!

Act out a scene with some friends using the following sentences and words at least once.

1 'I am a fish!'
2 'Help! Help! My head's made of wood!'
3 'Cost-efficiency!'
4 'Boy! Are we going to have a party!'
5 'Hello, I'm a computer scientist, please wake up!'
6 'Excuse me, am I allowed to feed the ducks?'

To help you, here are some suggestions for characters and places. Feel free to swop and change!

Character	Place
The Queen	A Rubbish Dump
Frank Bruno	Madame Tussaud's Waxworks!
Jim Bowen (from 'Bullseye!')	A Ferret-breeding farm
Terry Wogan	A Home for the Elderly
Madonna	In a Church
Your Next Door Neighbour	In Australia

Use the sentences, characters, and places in all of their many different forms and soon you'll be a 'Good Actor'! Have fun – and remember:
Don't Make Too Much Noise!

JOIN THE DOTS!

A

14 15 1

13

12

.2

.3

.4

.5

11

10

9 8 7 6

What shape is this?
Join the dots to see!

B

1 2 3 4 5 6 7 8 9 10 11 12

Join these dots
for lots of fun!

C

.
1

Fun!
For people without pens

D

1 2 3 .4
12 9 5 .6
13 11 .7
14 10 .20
.15 8 19
16 17 18 22 23 24 .25
21 26

Colour these dots!
Great fun!

E Join the pots!
(not much fun here!)

1
2
3
4
5

PALM READING
...for beginners

CAN YOU READ THIS PALM?

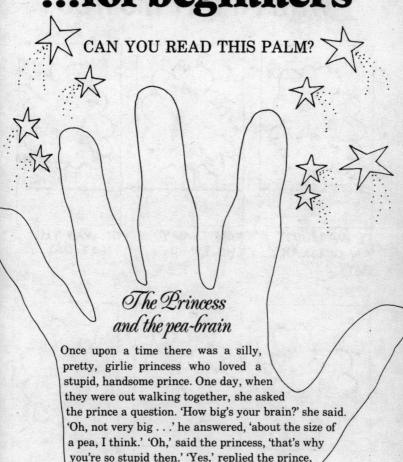

The Princess
and the pea-brain

Once upon a time there was a silly, pretty, girlie princess who loved a stupid, handsome prince. One day, when they were out walking together, she asked the prince a question. 'How big's your brain?' she said. 'Oh, not very big . . .' he answered, 'about the size of a pea, I think.' 'Oh,' said the princess, 'that's why you're so stupid then.' 'Yes,' replied the prince, and they lived happily ever after.

THE END

CARTOON FUN...
with TIMMY the Tree

IT WAS JUST
AN ORDINARY
DAY...

FOR TIMMY
THE TREE...

SO WAS THE
NEXT DAY...

...AND THE NEXT

...AND THE NEXT.

EVERY DAY
WAS MUCH THE
SAME...

...THEN CAME AUTUMN.

THE END

Do you believe in GHOSTS?

ANSWER THE QUESTIONS IN THIS
FUN-FILLED QUIZ AND FIND OUT!!

1) A loud noise wakes you up in the middle of the night. Is it . . .
   a) the wind
   b) a ghost
   c) a bottom burp

2) Walking down a spooky lane, you suddenly feel very cold. Is it because . . .
   a) it's winter
   b) a ghost has just walked past you
   c) all your clothes have fallen off

3) When you look in the mirror you see the face of a monster! Is it because . . .
   a) the mirror is in fact a TV showing 'WOGAN'
   b) there is a ghost looking at you
   c) you are a monster

4) What would you do if you saw an apparition? Would you . . .
   a) close your eyes and then look again
   b) shout 'Ah! It's a ghost!' and run away
   c) look up 'apparition' in the dictionary

5) One day, everyday things start flying around the room. Is this because . . .
   a) you are in a bird aviary
   b) there is a poltergeist in your house
   c) gravity has gone

How did you do?

WELL OR BADLY?

If you answered . . .

Mostly 'A's
You don't believe in ghosts! You are very, very sensible and dull. You are so dull and boring you could probably win 'Mastermind', except you're so boring Magnus Magnethead would fall asleep before you answered the first question. Well done!

Mostly 'B's
Yes! You believe in ghosts and you're a scaredy old baby pants. Well done!

Mostly 'C's
You are a ghost. Well done!

Mostly 'D's
You were doing a different quiz. Well done!

Mostly 'E's
Well done!

Mostly 'F's
Oh dear! Your lovelife is looking a bit poor. Everyone thinks you are a really horrible person and nothing in your life will ever be any good. Well done!

NEXT WEEK! DO YOU GO TO THE TOILET?
Answer our fun-filled quiz and find out!
This isn't a magazine, it's a book, stupid!

POP PICS № 1

Here is a picture of
KYLIE MINOGUE.

Can you guess who it is?

WHAT'S MISSING FROM THESE PICTURES OF SIMON AND TREV?

(see next page)

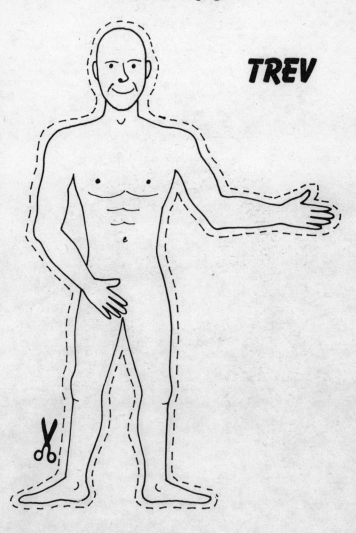

TREV

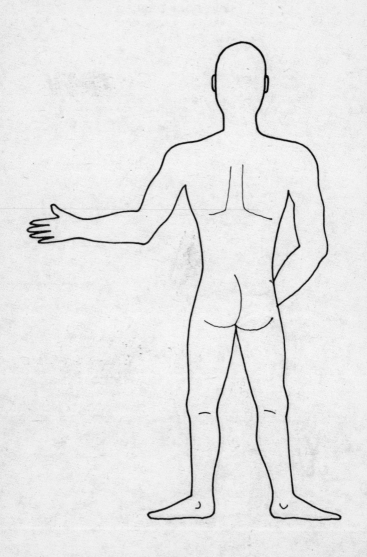

. . . THAT'S RIGHT! . . . CLOTHES!!

Well and hair . . . and beards of course!

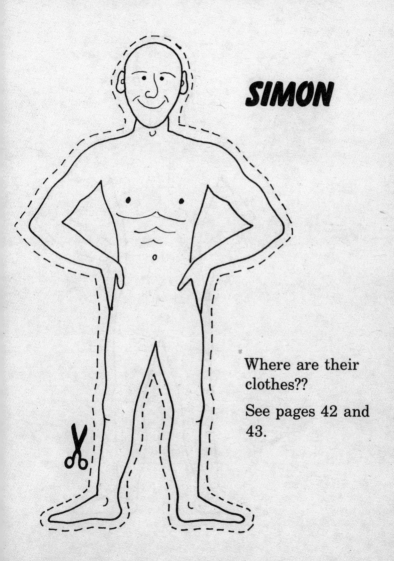

SIMON

Where are their clothes??

See pages 42 and 43.

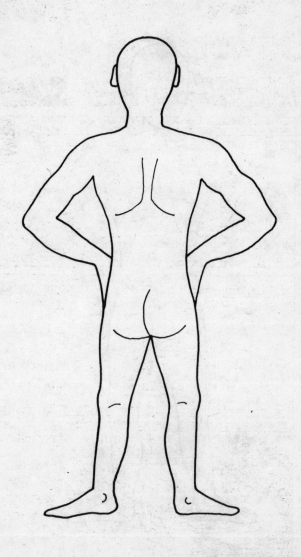

STUPIDMAN

STUPIDMAN AND THE PRESIDENT'S WALLET

IN A DISUSED WAREHOUSE A CRAZED MOB HAVE THE PRESIDENT OF THE UNITED STATES HOSTAGE, AND THEY WANT HIS WALLET...

OK, MR PRESIDENT, TELL ME WHERE YOUR WALLET IS OR I'LL USE THIS BOMB!

BOO HOO
YOU CAN'T DO THIS TO ME! I'M THE PRESIDENT OF THE UNITED STATES! THIS PLACE'LL BE SURROUNDED IN NO TIME AT ALL!
SOB

JUST GIVE US YOUR WALLET, CRY BABY!

MEANWHILE, OUTSIDE, THE POLICE COMMISSIONER AND LIEUTENANT BOJAK HAVE GOT THE PLACE SURROUNDED...

DISUSED WAREHOUSE

OK, BOJAK, WHAT DO THESE HOODLUMS WANT?

THEY WANT THE PRESIDENT'S WALLET, COMMISSIONER, AND THEY'VE GOT A BOMB!

A BOMB?!?

OK, BOJAK, JUST KEEP THINGS CALM AND QUIET AND WHATEVER YOU DO, DON'T CALL STUPIDMAN!

STUPID DETECTIVE BOLUMBO MAKES AN ANNOUNCEMENT...

YOU HEARD THE CHIEF! KEEP THINGS QUIET AND DON'T CALL STUPIDMAN!

NEARLY THE MIDDLE
OF THE BOOK

Well, here we are, past the middle of the book. It's time for a nice cup of tea! So go on; go and have a nice cup of tea. That's right − go and put the kettle on!

Put the book down for a bit and have a little break. You deserve it . . . Well go on then! . . . Go on!! . . . Oi!! Go on and make a cup of tea, you stupid bookworm!! . . .

OK, don't then . . .

Just forget it!

Well we're going . . . We're off for a nice cup of tea.

You can finish writing this page for yourself

HOW MANY FISH CAN YOU SPOT
IN THIS PICTURE?

Do you have trouble writing letters? Do you have friends you should have written to? Are you just too busy to sit down and write to them? Solve your problems **NOW** with this **INSTANT PERSONAL LETTER!**

Written with **sensitivity** and **feeling**, this letter can be photocopied **again and again!**

You'll never need to write another letter, as the carefully worded text means you can send the letter over and over . . . **even to the same person!**

Every time your friends receive the **INSTANT PERSONAL LETTER** we can guarantee their faces will light up with glee, and their hearts will glow, knowing they have a special friendship **for life!**

SEND IT NOW. . . and see the result!

INSTANT PERSONAL LETTER!

TO: A FRIEND

Date

Your name and
address here

Dear Friend,

Sorry I haven't written for a while,
but you know how time flies! How have
you been since I saw you last? Still
fit and well I hope!

Hasn't the weather been terrible recently?
Sometimes I think we should all go and
live in the Bahamas! Ha! Ha!

I really enjoyed our last day out together
at the 'Penine Way Fish Museum'! Did
you? I'll never forget that man who
kept impersonating a deadly pike!

Hope Jerome is still using the Indoor
Golfmaster Machine I gave him last
christmas! Give my regards to the
Reverend,

Yours sincerely,

Your signature here!

The 'B' Game

Here's a game that's very nearly **LOTS OF FUN!!!**

It's a simple game that anyone can play! Just follow this step-by-step guide!

1 Think of a word. Here's an example – **Video!**

2 Now replace the first letter of that word with the letter B – **'Bideo!'** Now say it out loud!

3 By now you should be laughing your head off, because the word sounds so **blinking funny!!!**

NOTE
If you choose a word that already begins with the letter **B**, like **bath**, you may be missing the joke a bit! Why not choose another word instead! However, you may have chosen the word **bottom** in which case you would be laughing your head off anyway – it's always a lot of fun to say **bottom** out loud!!!

Why not use **The B Game!** to have some fun in everyday conversations:

  'Can I have a cup of **boffee** please?'
  'How much is this warm winter **boat**?'

NOW TRY TWO OR MORE WORDS IN ONE SENTENCE:
'Shall we put the **belevision** on, or would you rather listen to some **busic**?'

WHY NOT TRY REPLACING THE FIRST LETTER OF ANY WORDS YOU FEEL LIKE WITH THE LETTER 'B'?
'Oh **bear**, I **bon't beel bell**!'

DON'T FORGET – It's more fun when you say these words out loud, especially when you're walking down a busy street on your own, or when you're on a bus, or when you are talking to *official people!*

SPOOKY THINGS TO MAKE. WHOOOOOH!

Well, it's probably nearly Halloween again, so why not make something spooky!!! Most people do the usual 'Spooky Pumpkin Head', but that's not really spooky, that's just rubbish.

A Spooky Pumpkin Head! Can you see how rubbish it is?

So . . . What's *really* Spooky???

Well . . . Margaret Thatcher is, but we won't talk about her now. After all, we don't want to spook ourselves stupid, do we?!? No!

So, here are some great spooky ideas! Oh, by the way, don't forget to say 'WHOOOOOO!' a lot! Because that's really spooky!!!

1 SPOOKY GRAPEHEAD!!!

WHOOOOOOO!

ACTUAL SIZE!
(Make one of these, then squash it!)

To make your **SPOOKY GRAPEHEAD** (Whooooo . . . it's spooky!), get a grape and hollow it out. Then cut out the eyes and the mouth. (You might need some micro-precision instruments for this.) Then get a tiny fibre optic light and push it inside . . . and that's it. Simple but spooky!!!

2 SPOOKY VIDEO CASSETTE HEAD!!!

"WHOOOOOOO!"

NOT ACTUAL SIZE
(or actually
very good!)

How do you make this **SPOOKY VIDEO CASSETTE HEAD**? Well, it's easy! Get a video cassette (a dodgy old one with a rare recording of something really valuable and special to someone in your family will do . . . no, not really . . . only do this if you like being beaten up severely!)

The best thing to do is to get an old broken video cassette (you could always break one when no one's looking . . . well, only if you like being locked in a cupboard with no food or water for six years!)

Now that you've got your video cassette . . . just make it! Simple but spooky!!! Whooooooooooh!!!

3 SPOOKY WIRE COATHANGER HEAD!!!

ACTUAL SIZE
(Sort of!?!)

How do you make the **SPOOKY WIRE COATHANGER HEAD**? Simple! Just use your imagination for a change and stop expecting us to tell you all the time! See! Simple but spoooooooky! Whooooooooo!!

OTHER IDEAS

SPOOKY PEA HEAD!!!

'WHOOOOOOOOO!'

ACTUAL SIZE
(but not actual flavour)

SPOOKY MICRODOT HEAD!!!

WHOOOOOOOO!

A bit bigger than actual size!

SPOOKY MICROWAVE HEAD!!!

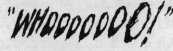

ACTUAL PIES

What about a . . . .

SPOOKY MATT BLACK PERSONAL
ORGANISER HEAD!!! Whooooooooooooooo!!

SPOOKY EMPTY BOX THAT YOUR PAIR OF
'I WISH I'D NEVER BOUGHT THEM NOW'
STEEL TOE-CAPPED RED AND BLACK
WITH THE WATCHES ON THE FRONT BROS
SHOES CAME IN, HEAD!!!
Whooooooooooooooo!!!

'**SWING YOUR PANTS**'® is the stupid catchphrase invented by those two stupid dimbos, **The Singing Corner!**

Occasionally other people come up with their own stupid versions of this popular catchphrase!

DON'T be fooled by these catchphrases! Only use the official **Singing Corner** catchphrase! (Unless you don't want to!)

LOOK OUT for these **BOGUS** catchphrases!

   SHAKE YOUR PANTS!
   SWING YOUR TROUSERS!
   SWIVEL YOUR JEANS!
   WIGGLE YOUR UNDIES!
   WASH YOUR KNICKERS!
   CHASE YOUR CHICKENS!

REMEMBER – If you can't **SWING YOUR PANTS!** then just **STAND STILL!**

HEALTH WARNING! – MOST DOCTORS DON'T **SWING THEIR PANTS!**

DOCTOR, DOCTOR

Doctor, doctor,
I keep on seeing spots
in front of my eyes!
So you'd better go and see an
optician, get your eyes tested,
and maybe get some glasses!
Thank you, doctor!

Doctor, doctor!!!
Just a minute! Are you
a private patient?
No!
Sorry, come back next year!

Doctor, doctor,
I feel like a pair of curtains!
Go and see a psychiatrist then,
you flippin' nutter!

Doctor, doctor!
No, I'm Doctor Phibes,
Doctor Doctor's in the
next surgery!

Doctor, doctor, people keep ignoring me!
It's because you're boring, now get out!

Doctor, doctor,
There's a fly in my soup!
I'm sorry, you're on the
wrong page!

Doctor, doctor, I feel
like Bob Monkh

STOP

This page has become too stupid!

New Year Resolutions!

Every year, around about the time of January, everyone starts to think about **NEW YEAR RESOLUTIONS!**

If you're like us, you most probably make one up and forget it by **00.01 am, JANUARY 1st!**

NOBODY can keep a New Year Resolution! Just take a look at some of these **blinking rubbishy ones** from the past!!

'I resolve never to make another "Rocky" film!'
   Sylvester Stallone talking on the set of 'Rocky VIII'

'I resolve to look old this year!'
   Cliff Richard

'I resolve to never appear on television this year!'
   Terry Wogan

'I resolve to give up singing this year!'
   Cliff Richard

'I resolve to be kind to the elderly and sick this year!'
   Margaret Thatcher

'I resolve to bring out a good record this year!'
   Cliff Richard

'We resolve to be funny this year!'
   Trev and Simon (only joking ?!?)

See what we mean? Why not be more realistic and a have a **NEW MONTH RESOLUTION**, or even **NEW DAY RESOLUTION**. Or how about a **NEW MINUTE RESOLUTION** or perhaps a **NEW SECOND RESOLUT-** (OK, stop now, that's enough – The Editor!)

The SISTER BROTHERS COMPETITION TIME

Hello everyone out there in 'Give us something for nothing' land, it's us, Gary and Barry Sister, the Sister Brothers! We're flippin' crazy we are! Yeah! that's us, flippin' crazy! Wheelin' and a dealin', duckin' and a divin', thinkin' up and a settin' out tricky competition questions! Except this competition is dead easy, right, and it's got a flippin' brilliant prize!

Have you ever wondered what it's like to get punched in the face? Does it hurt or what? Well now *you* can find out, simply by entering our crazy competition! The first prize is – well, the only prize is . . . yeah, that's right . . . a punch in the face!!!

How do you enter? Easy! Just go out into a public place, go up to someone and ask them any one of the questions written out below!
    That's all you have to do!

Don't send your answers on a postcard and definitely don't send *anything* to us – in fact *don't* mention us at all to *anyone*!

Good luck! Here's the questions!
    If you ask any of these questions in the *correct* way we almost guarantee you will collect your prize *instantly*!

1 Excuse me, bottom-head, would you punch me in the face?
2 Are you Andrew Lloyd Webber?
3 (To a policeman) Have you got the time?
4 (To Frank Bruno) Oi, wanna fight?

Wordsearch

HIDDEN IN THIS JUMBLE
OF LETTERS ARE SEVERAL WORDS.

Can you find them?

```
K   K   K   K   K   K   K   K   K   K   K
K   B   O   G   E   Y   K   K   K   K   E
K   O   K   K   K   K   K   K   K   K   L
K   T   K   K   B   K   K   K   K   K   K
K   T   K   K   K   U   K   K   K   K   N
B   O   G   K   K   K   M   K   K   K   I
K   M   K   K   K   K   K   K   K   K   T
K   K   K   K   K   K   K   K   K   W   K
K   P   O   O   P   O   O   S   K   E   K
K   I   K   K   E   K   K   N   K   E   K
K   D   K   K   E   K   K   O   K   W   K
K   D   K   K   P   K   K   G   K   E   K
K   L   K   K   E   K   K   K   K   E   K
K   E   K   K   E   K   K   K   K   K   K
K   K   K   K   K   K   K   K   K   K   K
```

Tick-Tock Fun

Have you ever wanted your very own wristwatch? Well, now you can have one! With this cut-out and keep trendy wristwatch, you will always know the time, just when you need to!!

How does it work? Simple!!!

Cut out the watch and stick it round your wrist. Now ask someone the time.

Fill in the hands on your watch with a pencil* and there you go!!!

Impress your friends with your precise time-keeping ability, everywhere you go: at home, at work, in the office, in the bin.

* Pencil not included

Cut here along the dotted line. Perhaps you might want to colour your watch strap with a felt pen, for more fun!

Here are some spare faces. You may need them.

Digital. ➡
(Fill in the numbers)
Fun with technology!

Give Mickey Moose time-telling antlers!!

Funny letters

Many people often say to us, 'Trev! Simon! What is the funniest letter in the alphabet?' We then ask them, 'Why?' And they say to us, 'That's funny! We thought it was Q!'

Funny joke

Many people often say to us, 'Trev! Simon! What is the funniest joke that has ever been told?' And we always say the same thing, 'Mind your own business'.

Funny numbers

Many people often say to us, 'Trev! Simon! Do you know any funny sums?' And we always say, 'Yes! How about these?'

$$2 + 2 = 5$$
$$5 - 3 = \text{[bird drawing]}$$
$$\frac{4 + 10}{6} = \text{A Fish}$$

Funny words

Many people often say to us, 'Trev! Simon! What is the funniest word in the world?' One of us says, 'Plinth!' and the other says, 'Borrovan!' We just can't agree on this one!

Swing Your Pants Through History

Many famous speeches, that we all **think** we know so well, are often not the original words said by those **GREAT FIGURES IN HISTORY!**

We have spent many minutes with our noses stuck in dusty old **HISTORICAL DOCUMENTS** and **PAMPHLETS** just so we can bring you the true, original sayings of those **GREAT FIGURES IN HISTORY!**

NELSON: 'Kiss me, Hardy! . . . And swing your pants!'

HUMPHREY BOGART: 'Play it again, Sam . . . and swing your pants!'

NAPOLEON: 'Not tonight, Josephine, swing your pants!'

JULIUS CAESAR: 'Friends, Romans, Countrymen . . . Swing your pants!'

JOHN F KENNEDY: 'Ich bin ein Pants Swinger!'

GOD: 'Let there be light . . .   and swing your pants!'

STUPID CROSSWORD

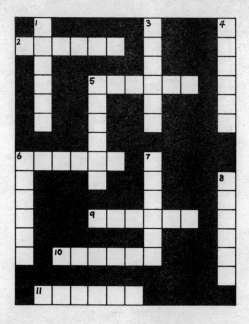

ACROSS

2 What this book is.

5 What this crossword is.

6 What you are if you're doing this crossword.

9 What you are if you're *still* doing this crossword.

10 Still doing it? OK then . . . Six-letter word meaning 'Stupid'!

11 Re-arrange these letters: D S T U P I

DOWN

1 See 9 across.

3 See 1 down.

4 See someone walking about in just their underpants and they will look — — — — — — .

5 Oh, you know what the answer is by now!

6 Yes, same again!

7 And again!

8 How you must be feeling by now!

NEVER
PLAY
WITH
F🐟SH!

Always treat fish sensibly.
Fish are not toys.
Fish are nice but they are <u>not</u> to play with.
Watch them ... even draw them.
But <u>never</u> play with fish.

Draw a fish here →

Why not cut this poster out and
pin it up in a public place?

COLOURING-IN FUN!!

HERE'S A PICTURE OF THE INVISIBLE MAN FOR YOU TO COLOUR

Letters Page

Mr. S. Cheese,
Cheddar St,
Stilton

Dear Trev and Simon,
I read your so called "Letters Page" with much disappointment! I was hoping for an interesting selection of ideas, opinions and points of view. What do I get? A load of old rubbish! Do you really think you can get away with stuff like that? Come on, Trev and Simon, you can do better!

Yours, Stephen Cheese

Can...
Potat...

Dear Trev and Si...
What was that Letters Page about? It was a complete waste of time. I read it over and over in case I was missing something but <u>no</u>...

Mrs P. Fruit
Banana St,
West Apple.

Dear Trev and Simon,
What an earth do you
think you were doing with
that "Letters Page". There wasn't
one decent piece of writing in the
whole thing. If you ask me,
you should have just printed a
load of old nonsense, it would
have been just as good, so

Rev. Palmsworthy
Little End Rd.
Holywell.

Dear Trev and Simon,
Can I congratulate you on a
fine "Letters page." I felt your
editorial judgement was superb. Let
the people have their say... That's what
I say! Very good idea

BACKWORD

Hello again!
Thanks for reading
"Trev and Simon's Stupid Book;'
Oh, and thanks for going to the trouble
of finding a mirror so that you can read this!
We hope you think it's good fun
because if you don't
then it's just one big fat waste of time!
OK, you can start to read the book again
now . . .
Well, go on then!
Oi!!!
Stop staring into the mirror like a stupid
zomboid monk, you big vanity-pants!

HAVE FUN!!!

APPENDIX

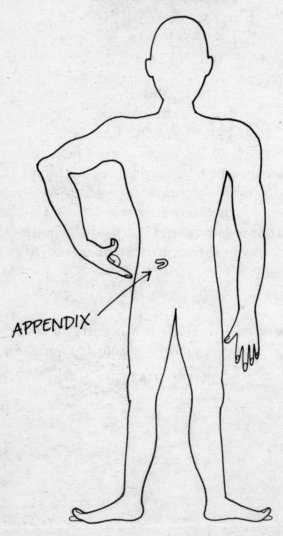

APPENDIX

KNOCK KNOCK FUN

Knock knock!!!
Who's there?
The police!
The police who?
Just open the door or
we'll knock it down!
Oh, OK then!

Knock knock!!!
Who's there?
Your best friend!
Come on in then!

Knock knock!!!
Who's there?
A Littlewoods representative. You've
won a million pounds on the 'pools'!!!
Oh, come on in then!

Knock knock!!!
Use the doorbell, I can't
hear you knocking!

Knock knock!!!
Who's there?
Doctor Doctor!
Doctor Doctor who?
Doctor Doctor there's a fly in my soup!
OK, come on in then!

Knock knock!!!
Who's there?
Margaret!
Margaret who?
Margaret Thatcher!
Oh, go away then!

Opportunity Knocks!!!
Who's there?
Bob Monkhouse
Oh, hello co

This page has become too stupid!!!

These two pictures are nearly identical.
However, there are FIVE differences.
Can you spot them?

WILDERNESS

AS PLAYED BY SIMON'S GRANDPA

A SPOOKY GAME FOR ALL THE FAMILY!!!

Here's a spooky game that anyone can play . . .
AS LONG AS THEY'RE BRAVE ENOUGH!!!

How many can play WILDERNESS???

As many as you want! But it must involve at
least ONE.

Where do you play WILDERNESS???

WILDERNESS is best played in a car, at
night, but you could also play wherever there is
a window which looks out into the empty
DARKNESS OF NIGHT-TIME!
    The countryside is a good place! or why not
play **WILDERNESS** while driving along an
empty motorway or country lane!
    Remember, if you're in a car, the driver *can't*
play! They have to keep their eyes on the road!
But you . . . you can look out into . . . the
WILDERNESS!!! (Unless 'you' are the driver,
in which case you can't play either.)

How to play WILDERNESS!

Press your face close to the window or rear
window of the car and look back into the empty
DARKNESS OF NIGHT-TIME! Then slowly
and spookily chant the words '**WILDERNESS,
WILDERNESS!!**' over and over and over again!
Not too loud, not too quiet! But with a deep
voice like a **GHOST!!!**

How do you win WILDERNESS???

It is impossible to win at **WILDERNESS** because it's just not that kind of a game! It's just **SPOOKY** fun!!! But for those of you who have to be so flippin' competitive all the time, why not play like this:

A Until nobody can stand playing it any longer – the last one to keep chanting **WILDERNESS** is the winner!

B Until the driver of the car goes mad because they're sick of hearing everyone else chant **WILDERNESS** while they have to be all boring and responsible!

C Until something leaps out of the **WILDERNESS** and frightens everyone to bits! In this case the **THING** that leaps out of the **WILDERNESS** is the winner!

D Until your heads explode!

E Until it's daylight!

Have fun!!!

PET'S PAGE (who is pet?)

Pets can be great fun! (Unless your pet is an amoeba). Sometimes, though, pets can be expensive to look after properly. Sometimes keeping certain pets is just cruel. For example . . . never, never keep an elephant in a goldfish bowl.

So . . . if you want a pet but don't want the hassle then why not make one?

Follow this detailed, step-by-step, guide to make yourself a *stick insect*. Home-made stick insects are one of the easiest pets to keep and in return, you will have a friend for life!

HOW TO MAKE A STICK INSECT

1. Get an old jam jar and wash it out.
2. Puncture the lid of the jam jar to make some 'air-holes'.
3. Put some leaves inside the jar.
4. Find an old stick and put that in as well.
5. Invite your friends round and tell them it's a stick insect.
6. Shake the jar occasionally to make it look like it's moving.

WARNING If you have particularly clever friends, they may discover that your pet is just an old stick. If this happens, do the following . . .

1. Cry and tell them it's dead.
2. Shout 'Oh no! it's escaped!' And then cry a lot.
3. Just cry a lot until they go home.
4. Fall to the floor and bang your fists on the ground, shouting 'I'm stark raving flippin' mad' and then let out a really weird high pitched whining sound until *they* cry a lot.

FUNNY GOOSE!

Here's a funny, friendly goose.

Can you think of a name for it?

Have some fun thinking of different names.

Write the name in this box.

Honk! Honk!

Here're some useful suggestions to help you get started:

FUNNY GOOSE

GOOSEY

HONKEY

MICHAEL

MADONNA

JAMES ANDERTON

The Singing ♫ ♪
Corner ♪ ♫

Stupid haircuts

Stupid beards

Stupid sandals

Stupid green cords Semi-flared

Stupid knitted brightly coloured jumper

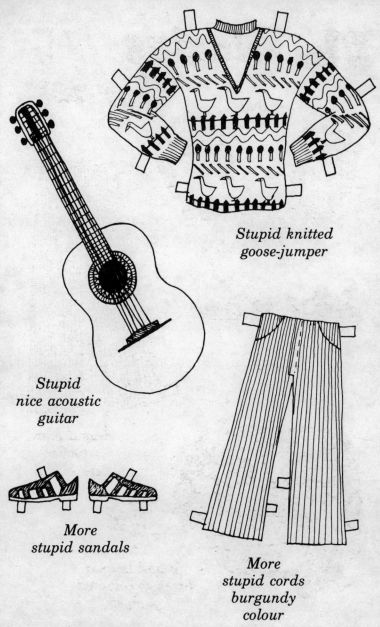

*Stupid knitted
goose-jumper*

*Stupid
nice acoustic
guitar*

*More
stupid sandals*

*More
stupid cords
burgundy
colour*

43

WEAR NUKE...

AND YOU WILL NEVER WEAR
ANOTHER PAIR OF TRAINERS AGAIN!

NUKE
THE LAST WORD IN
SPORTSWEAR.

PAINT BY NUMBERS

COLOUR THIS LOVELY SNOW SCENE
USING THE NUMBERED GUIDE BELOW

1 BLUE
2 WHITE
3 RED

4 YELLOW
5 GREEN
6 ORANGE

Hidden in this picture
are ten playful little kittens.
Can you spot them?

SNOOKER

Some people like snooker!

If *you* like snooker, why not read this step-by-step guide on how to enter the glamorous world of Professional Snooker. Soon you'll be up there with the full-time champs!

STEP ONE – THE NAME

Choose a good snooker name. Here's a list of names to help you choose:

Jimmy 'Whirlwind' White

Alex 'Hurricane' Higgins

Simon 'Windy' Hickson

Trev 'Cloudy with Scattered Showers' Neal

Dickie 'Stupid Hairstyle' Davies

Janet 'Street' Porter

Simon 'Le' Bon

Etc, Etc.

STEP TWO – THE CUE

A *A good homemade cue*

B *A good quality cue*

C *A snake*

If you have **Cue A** you will never be any good at snooker so don't bother trying!

If you have **Cue C** be very careful! Snakes can be poisonous!

If you have **Cue B** you are well on your way to winning the World Title!

STEP THREE – THE CLOTHES

It is very important when you are playing snooker to wear clothes!

STEP FOUR – THE TABLE

Getting a snooker table can be quite tricky. Here are the options:

A Buy a snooker table for £5000.

B Pay someone a lot of money to use their snooker table.

C Give up snooker

D Become Steve Davis.

STEP FIVE – THE LESSONS

Unless you become Steve Davis, you will need lessons in snooker. This will still involve Steve Davis so make sure you have his telephone number handy. Here's what to do:

Phone Steve Davis and ask him to teach you.

Now you are well on your way to winning that oh-so-important World Title!

STEP SIX – THE WORLD CHAMPIONSHIP

This is the big one! If you've got this far you won't need our help now. Just remember, smile a lot and do something funny, so that the TV people can put it in their funny comedy film at the end of the Championship. Here's some tips on how to be funny playing snooker:

A Climb on the table!

B Pretend to move the white ball!

C Scratch your nose!

D Scratch your bottom!

E All of the above at once!

STEP SEVEN – THE CHALK

Don't forget some chalk.
Good luck!!!

What is 'BORROVAN'?

Can you guess which is the 'real' **BORROVAN** from the pictures below?

Is **BORROVAN**

A A warm milky late night drink?

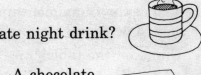

B A chocolate bar?

C A book?

D Fried corn bread?

E The surname of a 'Neighbours' star and heart-throb pop singer called Jason?

F The name of a sportswear company?

G A mobile home?

In fact, **BORROVAN** can be whatever you want it to be, because it doesn't really exist!

Why not have some fun seeing how many other things you can think up that could be called **BORROVAN**! We think it will keep you entertained for several fun-filled seconds!!!

HAVE YOU SEEN THIS MAN?

If you see **THIS MAN** Run away immediately!

He is wanted for several offences

Including:

1 **STUPID HAIRSTYLE!**
2 **STUPID BEARD!**
3 **STUPID SHIRT!**
4 **STUPID TIE!**
5 **STUPID EXPRESSION!**
6 **FAILING TO STOP BEING STUPID!**

LET'S BE SERIOUS

(and also a bit stupid)

When we were asked to write this book, we asked, 'Will the book be printed on recycled paper?'

They said ('they' being the big cheeses in the powerful world of publishing) 'Um . . . er . . . We don't know . . . we'll find out!'

We hoped it would be, because in the future if people asked us 'Hey, Trev and Simon, what did you do when we used to live on a planet that had trees?', we could say 'Well, actually, we tried to keep a natural balance between what we took from the Earth and what we put back, instead of just chopping down trees like crazy!'

Or something equally impressive and smug!

Unfortunately they ('they' being the big fish in the pulpy world of paper manufacturing) hadn't got their act together when it came to recycling the stuff!

So . . . Are you still awake? Good!

So . . . the big cheeses from the powerful world of publishing, having spoken to the big fish in the pulpy world of paper manufacturing, told us —

'Sorry, Trev and Simon, recycled paper comes in two kinds':

1 – Very poor quality!

2 – Very good quality!

Our book, being very mediocre, could not be printed on either! So that was that!

Sorry!

We did try!

RECYCLED PAPER

HOW TO SOLVE THE PROBLEM!

1 Write to your MP and tell them how stupid it is that recycled paper isn't easily available.

2 Phone your MP and tell them the same thing, explaining that you thought it would save paper using the telephone.

3 Cut out this page of the book and send it to your MP saying that they should read it.

4 Become an MP and do something about it yourself.

5 Become a tree.

6 Do *all* of these and then have a rest.

FUNNY CLOWN

Start scribbling here

Everyone loves a funny clown . . . except us!

Here's your chance to make up your own mind.

Do you love this funny clown? If you don't, why not scribble all over it with a crayon!

(Don't do this with other books, though, unless you want to get into a lot of trouble with the police.)

HA HA

HA HA

HA HA

HA HA

HA HA

HA HA

HA HA

HA HA

More scribbling can be done here

WATER

Here's some scribble to help you

Lots of room for scribble here

The Singing Corner

presents

FUN WITH BEARDS!

HELLOOOOOOOOOOO!!!

Do you have a beard? We do! We have one each! Sometimes we look around and wonder why everyone doesn't have a beard, just like ours! Would you like one? Goooooood!!!

Here's your chance to have a smashing beard! The first stage is to simply cut out the beard below and attach it to a stick*

Beard on a Stick

*We couldn't include a free stick with this book, so you will have to find one yourself. Don't worry, it's easy to find a decent stick!

CUT-OUT-AND-KEEP
'BEARD-ON-A-STICK!'

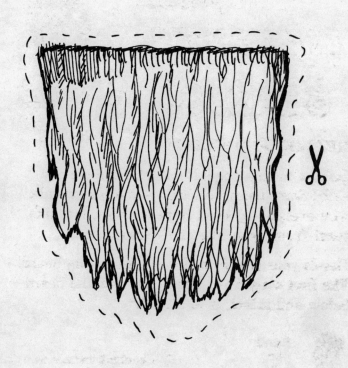

HOW TO USE YOUR
'BEARD-ON-A-STICK'

When you've made your own 'Beard on a Stick' you'll probably want to use it! All you have to do is take hold of your 'Beard on a Stick' and then place the beard end on your chin (see the easy to follow diagram below). It's easy, and so much FUN!!!

Why not colour your stick to match your shirt or sweater! This might make the stick seem invisible and so convince people your beard is real!!!

When placing the beard on your chin, be careful not to miss and put it up your nose! This will look like you have excess nasal hair, instead of a good beard!!!

MORE FUN WAYS TO USE YOUR

'BEARD-ON-A-STICK'

1 Place your beard on someone else's chin and see how they look! (Don't worry if they already have a beard of their own . . . See what a 'Two Bearded' person looks like!)

2 Sit in front of your TV and when your favourite showbiz celebrity comes on see what they look like with a beard!

This will also make boring old news and current affairs programmes much more fun! Just imagine, the Chancellor of the Exchequer comes on TV to announce more economic measures and you can be on hand to liven things up a bit with your 'Beard on a Stick'!

3 Why not use your 'Beard on a Stick' as a feather duster to reach those tricky dusty corners in your home (be careful of cobwebs!)

4 Use your 'Beard on a Stick' to conduct the Royal Philharmonic Orchestra!

5 With two 'Beards on a Stick' you can give yourself strange antennae sticking from your head . . . People might think you're an alien!!!

6 Use your 'Beard on a Stick' to tap people on the shoulder and save yourself time and energy from having to reach forward!

7 Use your 'Beard on a Stick' as a paint brush! Don't bother to wash it afterwards – pretty coloured beards can be great fun too!!!

8 Think of other ways to use your 'Beard on a Stick'!

Don't forget! **You can always throw it away!!!**

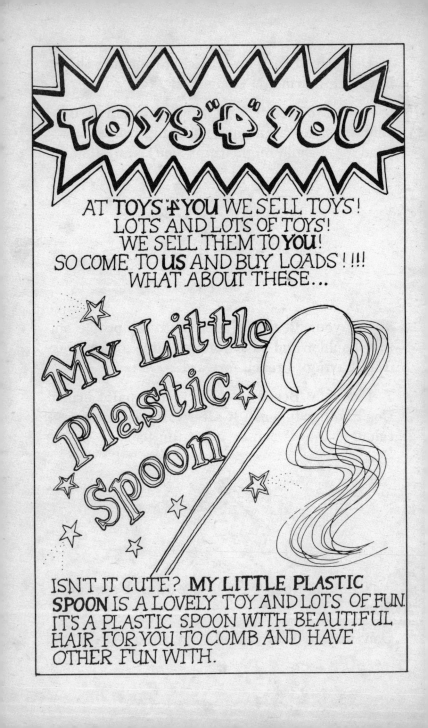